passages.

Blessing people at significant
moments in their lives
is a privilege that we can
all share, please use the
prayers in this book
to pray for those celebrating
occasions in the life
of the church.

The words of comfort in the
second part of the book may
be used at any time.
I hope you will find a prayer
or Bible passage that speaks
to you, and that you can
meditate on as you colour in.

x Mary

Baby and Child Blessing

In the name of the awesome God, who created you,
I pray protection over your life.
May your sleep be soaked in peace,
May your days be infused with love.

In the name of the Jesus, who is Love,
I pray wisdom over your life.
May you grow to seek God in all things,
May you meet God in the unexpected.

In the name of the Holy Spirit, our helper,
I pray joy over your life.
May you know the kindness of strangers,
May you find blessings in the small things.

BUT GROW IN THE GRACE AND KNOWLEDGE OF OUR LORD AND SAVIOUR
JESUS CHRIST. TO HIM BE GLORY BOTH NOW AND FOREVER! AMEN.
2 PETER 3:18 (NIV)

aptism

THEREFORE GO AND MAKE DISCIPLES OF ALL NATIONS, BAPTISING THEM
 THE NAME OF THE FATHER AND OF THE SON AND OF THE HOLY SPIRIT,
AND TEACHING THEM TO OBEY EVERYTHING I HAVE COMMANDED YOU.
AND SURELY I AM WITH YOU ALWAYS, TO THE VERY END OF THE AGE."
MATTHEW 28:19-20 (NIV)

Help [n.] Dear Lord,
to care too much,
to love too freely,
to pray unceasingly,
to forgive endlessly,
to laugh fearlessly,
to question,
to live,
to be who they are,
to be where they are,
to be what they are,
to hope,
to believe,
to reach out their hand.

[n.] = name

May Jesus teach you how to love, how to live in His presence.
May Jesus teach you how to live, how to pray in His will.
May Jesus teach you how to pray, how to rest in His embrace.
May Jesus teach you how to rest, how to be in His world.
May Jesus teach you how to be, how to love in His way.

Confirmation/First Communion

Today you take a giant leap into the depths of life,
Nothing will be the same.
Today you say 'yes' to seeing the world with new eyes,
Today you say 'yes' to serving your world with a humble heart,
Today you say 'yes' to ultimate living.

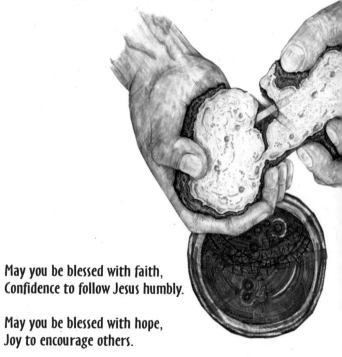

May you be blessed with faith,
Confidence to follow Jesus humbly.

May you be blessed with hope,
Joy to encourage others.

May you be blessed with love,
Courage to care for your neighbour.

As you follow Jesus today,
May you, God's creation,
discover how to be creative.

As you follow Jesus today,
May you, God's child,
begin to understand how
you are precious.

As you follow Jesus today,
May you, God's new saint,
learn sacrifice and wisdom.

As you follow Jesus today,
May you, God's beloved,
accept love from others
and give love in return.

BUT SEEK FIRST HIS
KINGDOM AND HIS
RIGHTEOUSNESS, AND ALL
THESE THINGS WILL BE
GIVEN TO YOU AS WELL.
MATTHEW 6:33 (NIV)

Have I not
commanded you?
Be strong and
courageous.
Do not be afraid;
do not be
discouraged,
for the Lord your
God will be with
you wherever
you go."
Joshua 1:9 (NIV)

As you journey, may you travel towards Jesus,
As you need, may your cry be heard,
As you pray, may you hear God's will.
As you breathe, may you give thanks,
As you believe, may your faith be infectious,
As you pray, may you hear God's will.
As you love, may your love be unlimited,
As you praise, may your spirit dance freely,
As you pray, may you hear God's will.

Ordination/Commissioning

May the blessing of joy be yours today,
And each new day,
The joy of following the call.

May the blessing of peace be yours today,
And each new day,
The peace of obeying the call.

May the blessing of confidence be yours today,
And each new day,
The confidence of embracing the call.

God give you the gift of faith,
That you may serve humbly.
God give you the gift of hope,
That you may minister cheerfully.
God give you the gift of love,
That you may care passionately.

THEREFORE GO AND MAKE DISCIPLES OF ALL NATIONS, BAPTISING THEM
IN THE NAME OF THE FATHER AND OF THE SON AND OF THE HOLY SPIRIT,
AND TEACHING THEM TO OBEY EVERYTHING I HAVE COMMANDED YOU.
AND SURELY I AM WITH YOU ALWAYS, TO THE VERY END OF THE AGE."
MATTHEW 28:19-20 (NIV)

Thank you for this moment,
May it be sacred,
O God,
make it Yours,

Thank you for this life,
May it be ready,
O God,
make it Yours,

Thank you for this voice,
May it be prayer,
O God,
make it Yours.

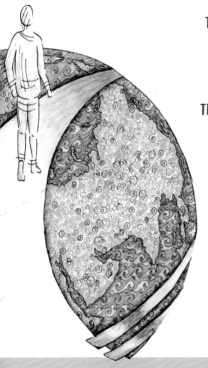

"HAVE I NOT COMMANDED YOU? BE STRONG AND COURAGEOUS.
DO NOT BE AFRAID; DO NOT BE DISCOURAGED, FOR THE LORD
YOUR GOD WILL BE WITH YOU WHEREVER YOU GO."
JOSHUA 1:9 (NIV)

Wedding

May you always remember
The 'why' of today,
May you always cherish
The memory of today.

May you always
Talk together,
Laugh together,
Play together,
Pray together.

May God be your guide and your glue

May you always
Strengthen each other,
Have time for each other,
Find peace in each other,
Respect each other.

May Love be your reason and your aim

TWO ARE BETTER THAN ONE,
BECAUSE THEY HAVE A GOOD RETURN FOR THEIR LABOUR:
IF EITHER OF THEM FALLS DOWN, ONE CAN HELP THE OTHER UP.
BUT PITY ANYONE WHO FALLS AND HAS NO ONE TO HELP THEM UP.
ALSO, IF TWO LIE DOWN TOGETHER, THEY WILL KEEP WARM.
BUT HOW CAN ONE KEEP WARM ALONE?
THOUGH ONE MAY BE OVERPOWERED, TWO CAN DEFEND THEMSELVES.
A CORD OF THREE STRANDS IS NOT QUICKLY BROKEN. ECCLESIASTES 4:9-12 (NIV

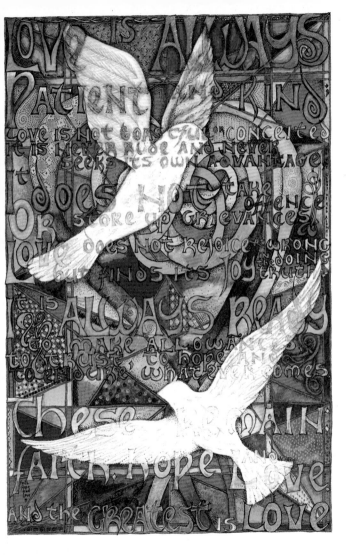

May your LOVE be PATIENT,
May your LOVE be KIND,
May your LOVE be SATISFIED,
May your LOVE be VULNERABLE,
May your LOVE be HUMBLE,
May your LOVE be HONOURABLE,
May your LOVE be GENEROUS,
May your LOVE be CALM,
May your LOVE be FORGIVING,
May your LOVE be HONEST,
May your LOVE ALWAYS PROTECT,
May your LOVE ALWAYS TRUST,
May your LOVE ALWAYS HOPE,
May your LOVE ALWAYS PERSEVERE,
May your LOVE NEVER FAIL.

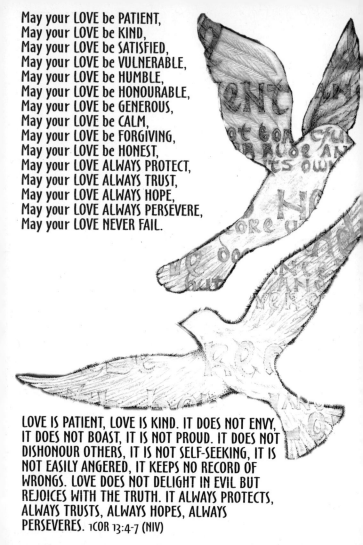

LOVE IS PATIENT, LOVE IS KIND. IT DOES NOT ENVY,
IT DOES NOT BOAST, IT IS NOT PROUD. IT DOES NOT
DISHONOUR OTHERS, IT IS NOT SELF-SEEKING, IT IS
NOT EASILY ANGERED, IT KEEPS NO RECORD OF
WRONGS. LOVE DOES NOT DELIGHT IN EVIL BUT
REJOICES WITH THE TRUTH. IT ALWAYS PROTECTS,
ALWAYS TRUSTS, ALWAYS HOPES, ALWAYS
PERSEVERES. 1COR 13:4-7 (NIV)

May
Love
Be
Your
Reason
And
Your
Aim

Comfort

Prayers, poems and Bible passages to encourage and reassure

Sometimes it's hard
to live out the life,
And be the person
we've been told we can be

Sometimes it's hard
to see the rainbow,
And not think
'It's just sunlight in rain'.

Sometimes it's hard.

God knows.

PEACE I LEAVE WITH YOU; MY PEACE I GIVE YOU. I DO NOT GIVE TO YOU AS THE WORLD GIVES. DO NOT LET YOUR HEARTS BE TROUBLED AND DO NOT BE AFRAID.
JOHN 14:27 (NIV)

WHEN JESUS SPOKE AGAIN TO THE PEOPLE, HE SAID, "I AM THE LIGHT OF THE WORLD. WHOEVER FOLLOWS ME WILL NEVER WALK IN DARKNESS, BUT WILL HAVE THE LIGHT OF LIFE."
JOHN 8:12 (NIV)

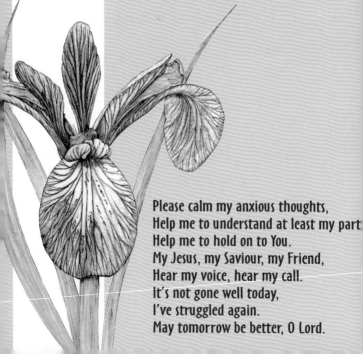

THE LORD IS MY
LIGHT AND MY
SALVATION -
WHOM SHALL I
FEAR?
THE LORD IS THE
STRONGHOLD OF
MY LIFE - OF
WHOM SHALL I
BE AFRAID?
PSALM 27:1 (NIV)

My Jesus, my Saviour, my Friend,
Hear my voice, hear my call.
It's not gone well today.

As the day winds down my mind spins around
So much I don't understand,
So much I'm holding on to.
My Jesus, my Saviour, my Friend,
Hear my voice, hear my call.
It's not gone well today.

Please calm my anxious thoughts,
Help me to understand at least my part
Help me to hold on to You.
My Jesus, my Saviour, my Friend,
Hear my voice, hear my call.
It's not gone well today,
I've struggled again.
May tomorrow be better, O Lord.

CONSIDER
HOW
THE
WILDFLOWERS
GROW

AND WHY DO YOU WORRY ABOUT CLOTHES? SEE HOW THE FLOWERS
OF THE FIELD GROW. THEY DO NOT LABOUR OR SPIN."
MATTHEW 6:28 (NIV)

EVEN THOUGH I WALK THROUGH THE DARKEST VALLEY
I WILL FEAR NO EVIL, FOR YOU ARE WITH ME;
YOUR ROD AND YOUR STAFF, THEY COMFORT ME.
PSALM 23:4 (NIV)

Grant me the faith to believe
That even when the path is hidden,
You will show me Your way
When the time is right.

I bind my mind to the mind of the Creator God
and I loose from my mind all that offends my God
that I may worship completely.
I bind my body to the will of the Saviour Christ
and I loose from my body all dis-ease
that I may serve freely.
I bind my spirit to the Holy Spirit my helper
and I loose from my spirit all that is not of my God
that I may love joyfully.

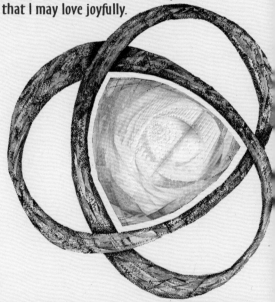

AND I WILL ASK THE FATHER, AND HE WILL GIVE YOU ANOTHER
ADVOCATE TO HELP YOU AND BE WITH YOU FOREVER - THE SPIRIT
OF TRUTH. THE WORLD CANNOT ACCEPT HIM, BECAUSE IT NEITHER
SEES HIM NOR KNOWS HIM. BUT YOU KNOW HIM, FOR HE LIVES
WITH YOU AND WILL BE IN YOU. JOHN 14:16-17 (NIV)

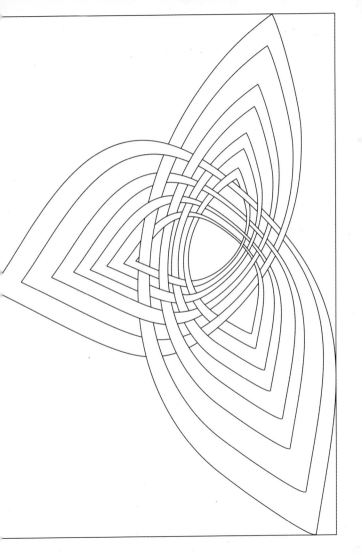

FOR GOD SO LOVED
THE WORLD
THAT HE GAVE
HIS ONE AND
ONLY SON,
THAT
WHOEVER
BELIEVES
IN HIM
SHALL NOT
PERISH
BUT HAVE
ETERNAL
LIFE.
JOHN 3:16
(NIV)

Circle me Lord, let love be my reason
Let hate be a stranger.
Circle me Lord, let joy be my comfort
Let sadness be no more.
Circle me Lord, let peace be my aim
Let conflict be resolved.